CANADIAN CURRICULUM PRESS
Forward Learning

Reading
Readiness
abc R

D1533413

Table of Contents

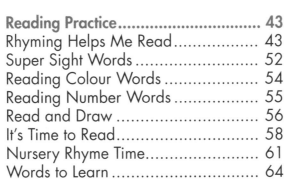

- Letters and sounds Aa to Zz
- Rhyming, sight words, word families
- Matching games
- Nursery rhymes
- And much more!

Margaret Ann Hawkins, B.Ed.

Ss Print S and s.

Ŝ S S S S S S

ŝ s s s s s

Look at the pictures. Print the beginning letter on each word. Read the word.

__s__ tar

___ pider

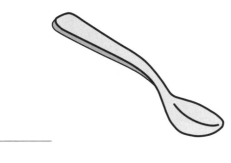

___ poon

___ wing

A a   Print **A** and **a**.

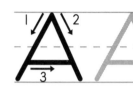

A A A A A

a a a a a a

Colour the pictures. Print the beginning letter on each word. Read the word.

___ nt

___ stronaut

___ pple

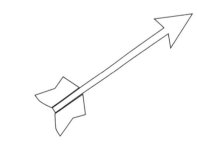

___ rrow

T t   Print T and t.

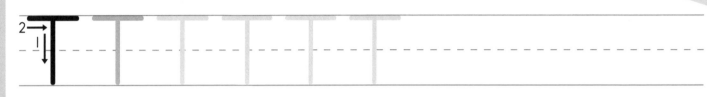

Look at the pictures. Print the beginning letter on each word.
Read the word.

____ eapot

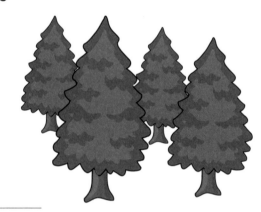

____ rees

____ ent

____ able

Ii   Print I and i.

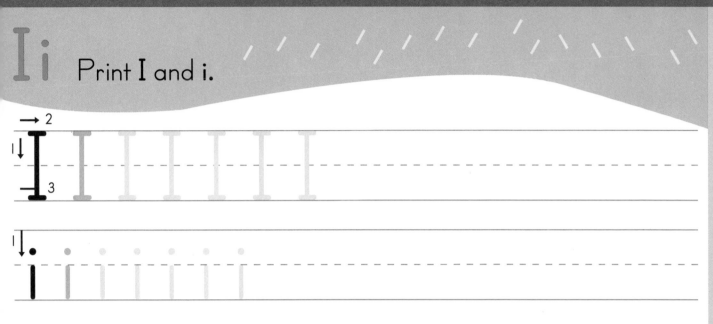

Colour the pictures. Print the beginning letter on each word. Read the word.

___gloo

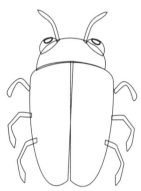

___nsect

___ce cream

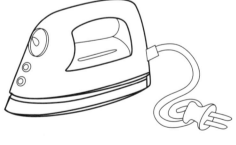

___ron

P p   Print **P** and **p**.

Look at the pictures. Print the beginning letter on each word. Read the word.

___ ig

___ ear

___ umpkin

___ izza

Nn Print **N** and **n**.

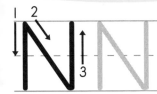

Colour the pictures. Print the beginning letter on each word.
Read the word.

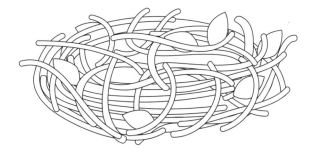

___ est

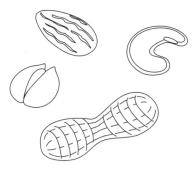

___ uts

___ ose

___ ine

Cc Kk   Print C and c, K and k.

C C C C C C

K K K K K K

c c c c

k k k k

Look at the pictures. Print the beginning letter on each word.
Read the word.

_ _ up

_ _ ar

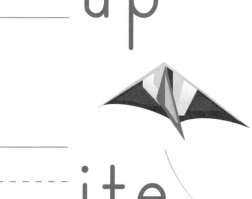

_ _ ite

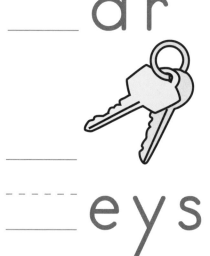

_ _ eys

Cut out the letters at the bottom. Glue the letters to finish the words. Read the words you made.

___tar

___ron

___nt

___ig

___ree

___est

a i n s p t

Connect the Dots

Start

Space for cutting on reverse side of page.

E e   Print **E** and **e**.

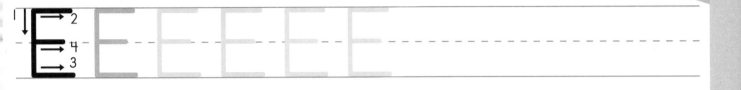

E E E E E E

e e e e e e e

Colour the pictures. Print the beginning letter on each word.
Read the word.

___ lbow

___ ar

___ lephant

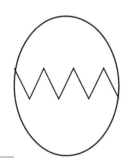

___ gg

Hh Print H and h.

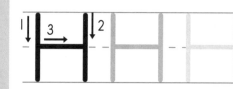

Look at the pictures. Print the beginning letter on each word. Read the word.

____at

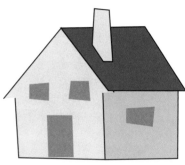

____ouse

____and

____orse

R r   Print **R** and **r**.

R R R R R R

r r r r r r

Colour the pictures. Print the beginning letter on each word. Read the word.

__acquet

__unning

__ooster

__ecycle

 Print **M** and **m**.

Look at the pictures. Print the beginning letter on each word. Read the word.

____ o o n

____ i t t e n s

____ o m

____ u f f i n

14

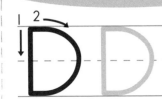 Print **D** and **d**.

 D D D D D

d d d d d d

Look at the pictures. Print the beginning letter on each word. Read the word.

____ olphin

____ ress

____ rum

____ og

G g Print G and g.

G G G G G

g g g g g g

Look at the pictures. Print the beginning letter on each word.
Read the word.

___ rapes

___ oat

___ host

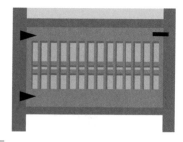

___ ate

Cut out the letters at the bottom. Glue the letters to finish the words. Read the words you made.

ar

gg

orse

abbit

oon

rum

c h d r e m

Connect the Dots

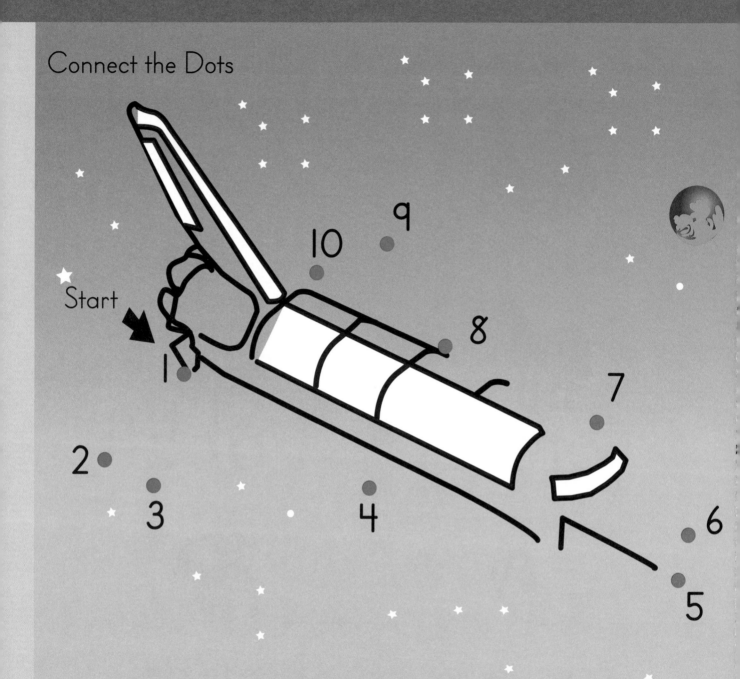

Start

Space for cutting on reverse side of page.

18

O o   Print **O** and **o**.

Colour the pictures. Print the beginning letter on each word.
Read the word.

___ range   ___ nion

___ n / ___ ff

U u   Print U and u.

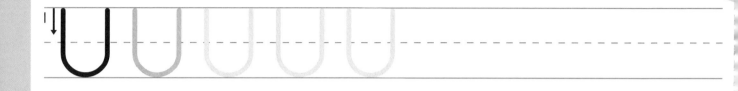

U U U U U U

u u u u u u u u

Look at the pictures. Print the beginning letter on each word.
Read the word.

___ mbrella

___ p

___ dder

___ nicorn

L l   Print L and l.

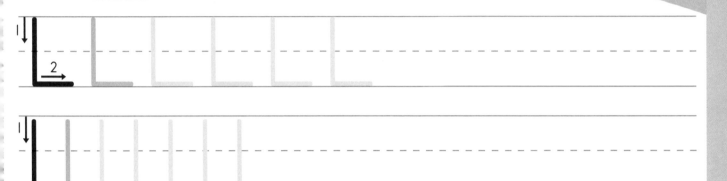

Look at the pictures. Print the beginning letter on each word. Read the word.

___emon

___ollipop

___ips

___eaf

F f Print **F** and **f**.

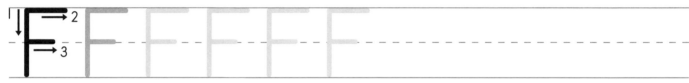

Look at the pictures. Print the beginning letter on each word.
Read the word.

____ l a g

____ i s h

____ i r e

____ e a t h e r

Bb   Print B and b.

B B B B B B

b b b b b b

Colour the pictures. Print the beginning letter on each word. Read the word.

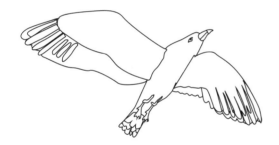

___ird

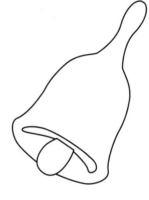

___ell

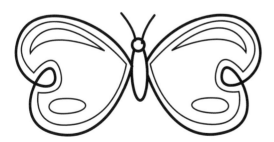

___utterfly

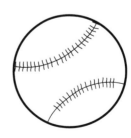

___all

Print J and j.

 J J J J J J J J

 j j j j j j j j

Look at the pictures. Print the beginning letter on each word.
Read the word.

____ acket

____ ump

____ am

____ uice

24

Cut out the letters at the bottom. Glue the letters to finish the words. Read the words you made.

rapes

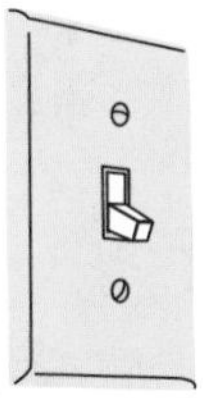

ff

p

ips

lag

ird

u g o b l f

Follow the dots from 1 to 10.
Colour the picture.

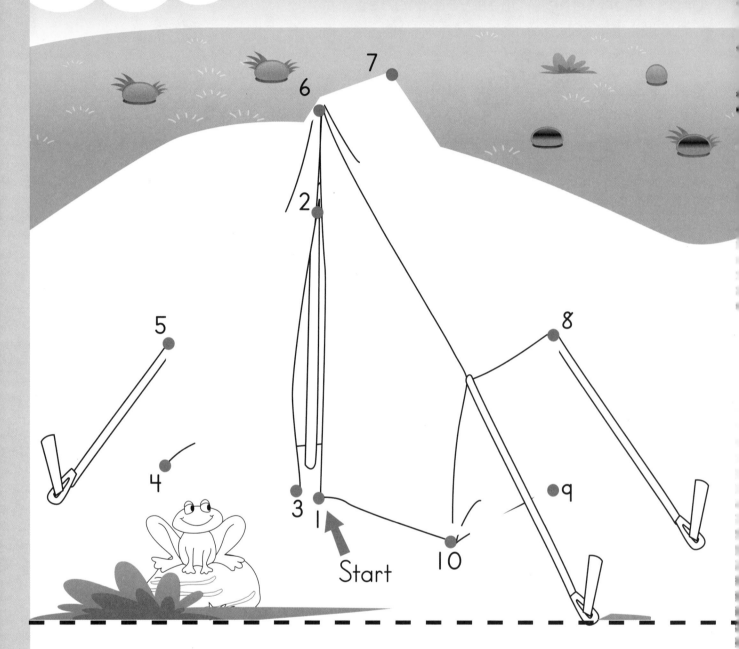

Space for cutting on reverse side of page.

Zz Print Z and z.

Z Z Z Z Z Z

z z z z z z z

Colour the pictures. Print the beginning letter on each word. Read the word.

___ ebra

O

___ ero

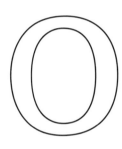

___ ig

___ ag

___ oo

W w   Print **W** and **w**.

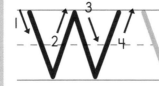

Look at the pictures. Print the beginning letter on each word. Read the word.

___atermelon

___e b

___ings

___orm

V v   Print V and v.

Colour the pictures. Print the beginning letter on each word. Read the word.

___ a s e

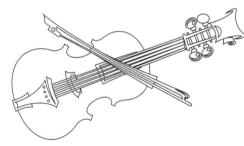

___ i o l i n

___ e s t

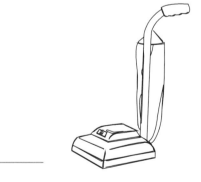

___ a c u u m

Print Y and y.

Look at the pictures. Print the beginning letter on each word. Read the word.

_____ o-yo

_____ arn

_____ am

_____ ogurt

X x Print X and x.

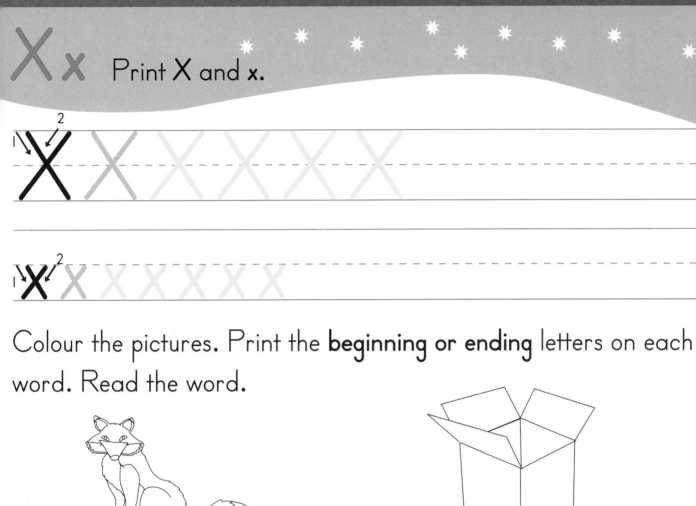

Colour the pictures. Print the **beginning or ending** letters on each word. Read the word.

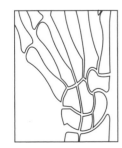

fo____

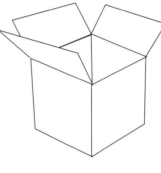

____ray

bo____

6

si____

CH ch Print **CH** and **ch**.

Look at the pictures. Print the beginning letters on each word. Read the word.

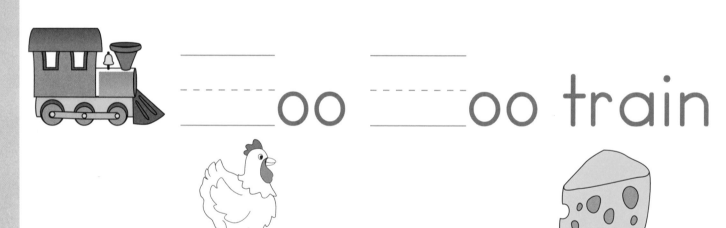

_____oo _____oo train

_____icken _____eese

_____ecker board

Cut out the letters at the bottom. Glue the letters to finish the words. Read the words you made.

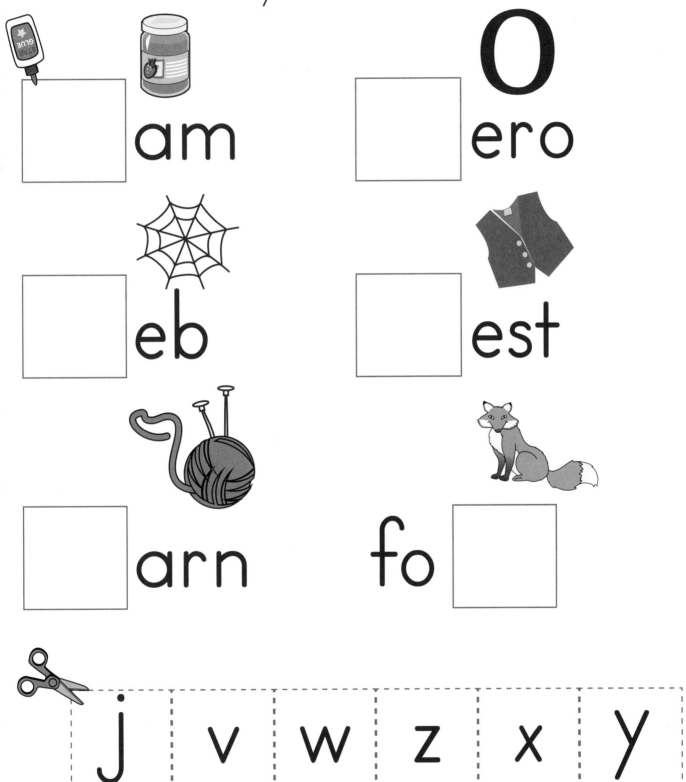

am

O ero

eb

est

arn

fo

j   v   w   z   x   y

Follow the dots from 1 to 10.
Colour the picture.

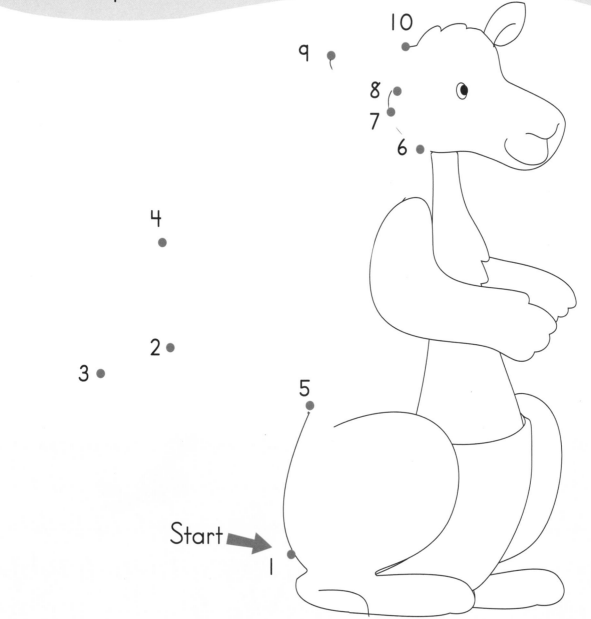

Start

Space for cutting on reverse side of page.

SH sh Print SH and sh.

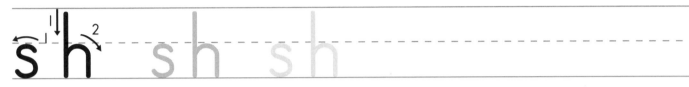

sh sh sh

Colour the pictures. Print the beginning letters on each word.
Read the word.

_____ eep

_____ ell

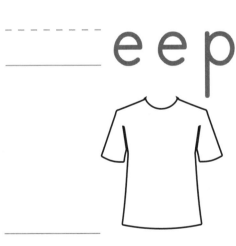

sh irt

_____ oe

35

TH th   Print TH and th.

Look at the pictures. Print the beginning or ending letters on each word. Read the word.

____imble   ____ree

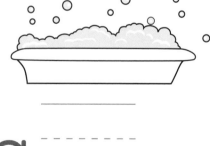

ba____   tee____

QU qu   Print QU and qu.

QU QU

qu qu

Colour the pictures. Print the beginning letters on each word. Read the word.

_ _ _ e e n

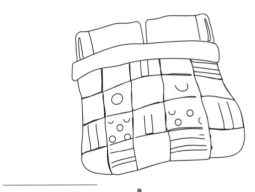
_ _ _ i l t

_ _ _ arter

_ _ _ ack

ING ing   Print **ING** and **ing**.

ING   ING

ing   ing

Look at the pictures. Print the ending letters on each word. Read the word.

swing _____

see _____

runn _____

play _____

ER er Print **ER** and **er**.

ER ER

er er er

Look at the pictures. Print the **ending** letters on each word. Read the word.

ski____

scoot____

surf____

flow____

AR ar   Print AR and ar.

Look at the pictures. Print the missing letters on each word. Read the word.

st____

c____

b___k

c___t

Cut out the letters at the bottom. Glue the letters to finish the words. Read the words you made.

eese

ell

3 ree

een

flow

st

ch sh th er ar qu

Colour me!

Space for cutting on reverse side of page.

Rhyming Helps Me Read  word family

This is a cat.

See how many words you can make that rhyme with cat.

Print the beginning letter to make the word.

Read the words you made.

c s r b h p m f

c at   ___ at

___ at   ___ at

___ at   ___ at

___ at   ___ at

Rhyming Helps Me Read

an word family

This is a fan.

See how many words you can make that rhyme with fan.
Print the beginning letter to make the word.
Read the words you made.

f b c p r t v m

f a n ___ a n

___ a n ___ a n

___ a n ___ a n

___ a n ___ a n

Rhyming Helps Me Read

en word family

This is a hen.

See how many words you can make that rhyme with hen.

Print the beginning letter to make the word.

Read the words you made.

h d m p t

h e n

10

___ e n

___ e n

___ e n

___ e n

Rhyming Helps Me Read

 **word family**

This is a nut.

See how many words you can make that rhyme with nut.

Print the beginning letter to make the word.

Read the words you made.

n g b h c r

n u t   _ u t

_ u t   _ u t

_ u t   _ u t

Rhyming Helps Me Read

ot word family

This is a pot.

See how many words you can make that rhyme with **pot.**

Print the beginning letter to make the word.

Read the words you made.

p g h d l n c r

p o t	_ o t
_ o t	_ o t
_ o t	_ o t
_ o t	_ o t

Rhyming Helps Me Read

ap

word family

This is a cap.

See how many words you can make that rhyme with **cap**.
Print the beginning letter to make the word.
Read the words you made.

c r g l m n s t

c a p	___ a p
___ a p	___ a p
___ a p	___ a p
___ a p	___ a p

Rhyming Helps Me Read

et word family

This is a net.

See how many words you can make that rhyme with **net.**

Print the beginning letter to make the word.

Read the words you made.

n b j g m l p s

___n e t   ___ e t

___ e t   ___ e t

___ e t   ___ e t

___ e t   ___ e t

Rhyming Helps Me Read

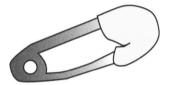

in word family

This is a pin.

See how many words you can make that rhyme with **pin.**
Print the beginning letter to make the word.
Read the words you made.

p w t f b k

p in   in

___ in   ___ in

___ in   ___ in

Rhyming Helps Me Read

 word family

See the dog sit.

See how many words you can make that rhyme with sit.
Print the beginning letter to make the word.
Read the words you made.

k   b   s   h   p

____ **s** it

____ it   ____ it

____ it   ____ it

Super Sight Words

These words will help you when you read.
Read each word. Draw a line to the matching word.

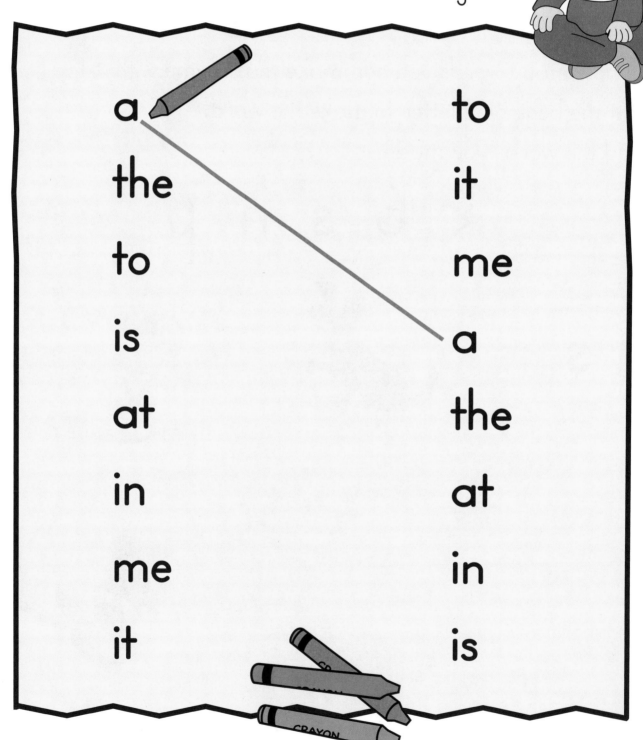

a	to
the	it
to	me
is	a
at	the
in	at
me	in
it	is

Super Sight Words

These words will help you when you read.
Read each word. Draw a line to the matching word.

Mom	love
Dad	girl
love	went
boy	Mom
girl	boy
went	look
play	play
look	Dad

Reading Colour Words

Colour each balloon the colour is says on it.

pink

green

orange

blue

purple

brown

white

yellow

red

Reading Number Words

1	2	3	4	5	6	7	8	9	10
one	two	three	**four**	five	**six**	seven	**eight**	nine	ten

Connect the dots from one to ten.

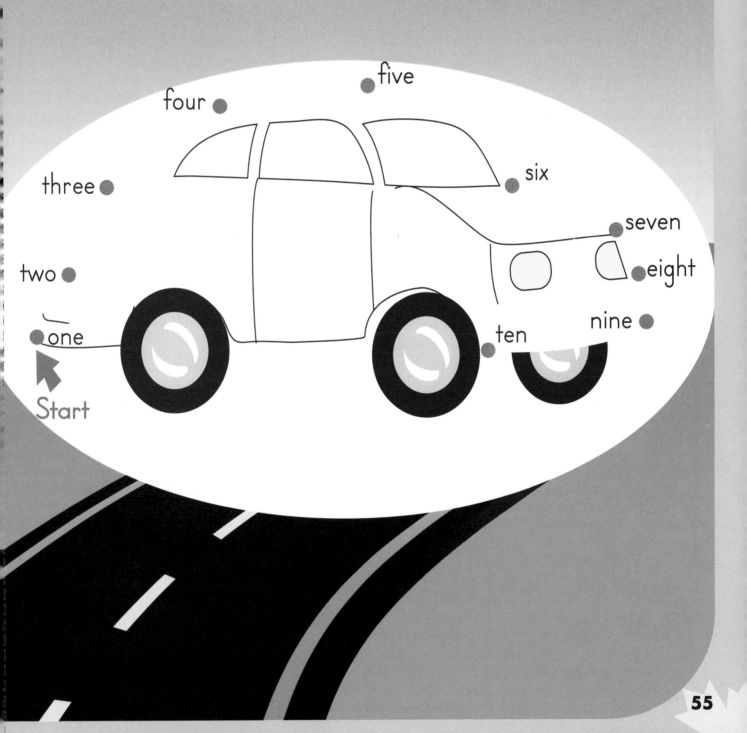

Read and Draw

Read the sentence.

Draw and colour a picture to go with each sentence.

He is at the playground.

She is in the pool.

Read and Draw

Read the sentence.
Draw and colour a picture to go with each sentence.

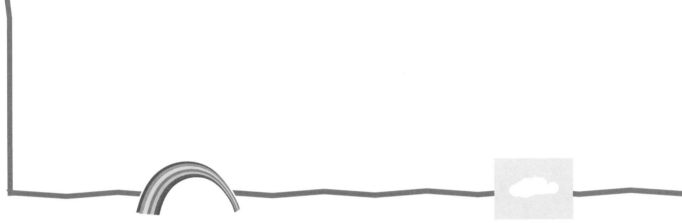

The rainbow is in the sky.

I have my umbrella in the rain.

It's Time to Read

Read the sentence.
Draw a line to match each sentence to a picture.

I see the slide.

The cat is orange.

He is at the park.

The sun is in the sky.

I am 5 years old.

It's Time to Read

Read the sentence.
Draw a line to match each sentence to a picture.

I see an apple.

The dog is black.

She is a girl.

The car is green.

It is raining.

It's Time to Read

Look at the picture.
Read the sentence. Print the missing word.

The bird _____ flying.

The _____ is in the house.

I like _____ swim.

I _____ fly a kite.

can   is   dog   to

Nursery Rhyme Time

Read the nursery rhyme.

Write the numbers 1, 2, 3, 4 to put the rhyme in order.

Hickory, Dickory, Dock

The clock struck one.

bong

The mouse ran down.
Hickory, dickory, dock.

Hickory, dickory, dock

The mouse ran up the clock.

Nursery Rhyme Time

Read the nursery rhyme.

Write the numbers 1, 2, 3, 4 to put the rhyme in order.

Jack and Jill

And Jill came tumbling after.

Jack fell down and broke his crown.

Jack and Jill went up the hill.

To fetch a pail of water.

Nursery Rhyme Time

Read the nursery rhyme.

Write the numbers 1, 2, 3, 4 to put the rhyme in order.

Little Miss Muffet

Along came a spider and sat down beside her.

( )

Little Miss Muffet sat on a tuffet.

(1)

Eating her curds and whey.

( )

And frightened Miss Muffet away.

( )

Words to Learn

Here is a list of high frequency sight words for children to learn to read by Grade 1.

Practice these early in the Kindergarten year.

These are more words for children to learn by Grade 1.

Practice these later in the Kindergarten year.

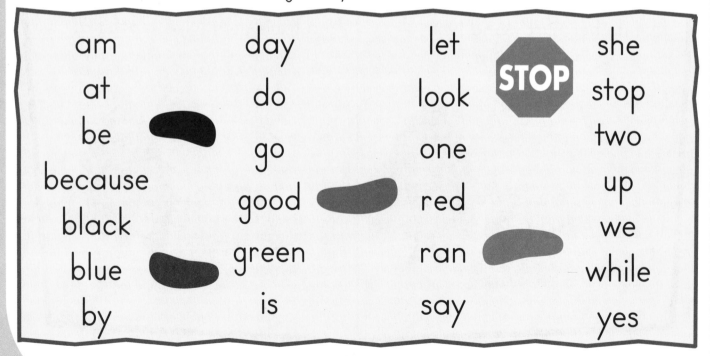